TWO
BASILS

Peter Firmin

FONTANA · LIONS

First published in Great Britain as separate volumes under the titles
Basil Brush Goes Boating
and *Basil Brush Goes Flying* 1969
by Kaye and Ward Ltd.

First published in Fontana Lions March 1982
by William Collins Sons & Co Ltd
14 St James's Place, London SW1

© 1969 Kaye and Ward Ltd.

Printed in Great Britain by
Richard Clay (The Chaucer Press) Ltd,
Bungay, Suffolk

BASIL BRUSH
GOES BOATING

Basil Brush is a well-dressed fox.
He looks very smart in his town clothes.

Basil Brush does not always wear his town clothes.

Sometimes he wears his football clothes,

or his rainy-weather clothes,

6

or his seaside clothes.

This is how he dressed when he went
boating with his friend Harry.
Harry is a mole.

They were going camping beside the
river. They took a boat, a tent and
some other things.

These are the things they took.

They took a bottle of lemonade,

a fishing net,
a basket,

a magnifying glass
(to study nature),

a frying pan

and a pair of canvas shoes.

"What else will you take?" asked Basil.

"I'll just take my black fur coat," said Harry.

"Well, you cannot leave it behind," said Basil.

"I know an island," said Basil. "On the island we can make a fire, cook our supper and sleep in our tent." "Let us go to that island," said Harry. Basil sat in the middle of the boat so that he could row. Harry sat at the back to work the rudder.

All their things were in the front.

They started up the river in their boat.

It was very hot.

"I am thirsty," said Harry.

Basil stopped rowing.

He passed the lemonade to Harry.

Harry said: "Have we a cup or some straws?" Basil looked at all their things. "We have a bottle of lemonade, a fishing net, a basket, a magnifying glass (to study nature), a frying pan and a pair of canvas shoes but we have no cup or straws."

"Never mind," said Harry.
"I will drink out of the bottle."

Harry drank out of the bottle.
Basil began to row. Harry rolled over
out of the boat into the water.

"Hold on, old chap," said Basil.
"I will scoop you out."
He scooped Harry out with the fishing net.

Harry soon dried out in the hot sun as
they rowed to the island.

They landed on the island and unloaded all their things.

They unloaded the tent, a fishing net, a basket, a magnifying glass (to study nature), a frying pan and a pair of canvas shoes.

Basil took the tent to a patch of grass.
"I will put up the tent," he said.
"And I will catch a fish," said Harry.
He ran off to catch a fish with the net.

Soon he caught a big striped fish.
He looked around for something to put
it in. There was nothing to put it in,
so he put it back in the water.

"Wait there, striped fish," he said.
"I will go back to get a jam jar."
He went to ask Basil for a jam jar.

Basil looked at all their things.

He said: "We have a basket, a magnifying glass (to study nature), a frying pan and a pair of canvas shoes, but we have no jam jar."

"Never mind," said Harry.

"I will make a fire."

He took the basket to get sticks for the fire and forgot about the fish.

Harry collected a big bundle of sticks.
It was too big for the basket so he
carried it on his head.

Harry made a big heap of the sticks.
"Basil," he said. "May I have the matches to light my fire?"
Basil looked at all their things.
"We have a magnifying glass (to study nature), a frying pan and a pair of canvas shoes, but we have no matches."

"Never mind," said Harry. "We can
make a flame with the magnifying glass.
We must shine the sun through it."
"You are a clever old mole," said Basil.
"But where is the sun?"

"I know," said Harry. "I saw the sun
on the other side of the island."
He took the magnifying glass and went
to find the sun.

He ran to the other side of the island
and climbed a tree stump.
The sun was going down behind the
river. "Sun," he called, "come back.
We need you!" But the sun did not
come back. Harry ran back to Basil.

"There is no sun now," he said sadly.
"It has gone down into the river."
"Never mind," said Basil.
"You get the supper ready. I will try
to make a spark by rubbing two sticks
together."

Harry took out the frying pan.
"Where are the sausages?" he asked.
Basil looked at their things.

"I see a frying pan," he said,
"and a pair of canvas shoes.
I cannot see any sausages."

"Never mind," said Harry. "I will find something to eat on the island, while you light the fire."
Harry took the frying pan and ran into the long grass.

In the reeds beside the water he saw
a mother bird sitting on a nest.
"Please could you let me have two eggs
for our supper?" he said.

The mother bird ran away.

Harry looked into the nest. Three baby birds were in the nest but no eggs.

Harry ran back to Basil.

"I am sorry," he said.

"I did not find anything to eat."

"It does not matter," said Basil,
"because I could not light the fire.
Now I am tired. Let us go to bed."

"I am tired too," said Harry.

"But where are the sleeping bags?"

Basil looked at their things.

"There is a pair of canvas shoes," he said, "but no sleeping bags."

"Never mind," said Harry. "It is a fine night. Let us take down the tent and use it for a sleeping bag."
So they took down the tent and wrapped it around them for a sleeping bag.

They slept soundly under the moon.
They slept until morning came.
When morning came it started to rain.

Basil put on his canvas shoes to keep his feet dry and they sat under the tent. "I do not like camping," said Harry. "I am cold and hungry. Let us go home." "If we hurry," said Basil, "we will be home in time for breakfast."

They ran with their things to the boat.

"Jump in," said Basil.

"I will push the boat out."

Harry jumped into the boat.
Basil took off his canvas shoes and
pushed the boat out into the river.
Then he jumped in too.

They floated very quickly down the river,
until they reached home.

They unloaded all their things.
They unloaded the tent.
There was nothing else . . .

because...

everything else was still on the island.

The little fishes live in
the lemonade bottle.

A blackbird sits
on her nest in the fishing net.

A family of wood-mice have their house in the basket.

The snail uses the magnifying glass (to study nature).

The frying pan makes a bath for the baby birds.

And the frogs have boat races in the canvas shoes.

"We seem to have left everything behind," said Basil, "except the boat and the tent!"

"And my black fur coat," said Harry.
"As you said, Basil, I cannot leave
that behind!"

the end

BASIL BRUSH
GOES FLYING

Basil Brush is a well-dressed fox.

He looks very smart in his town clothes.

Basil Brush does not always wear
his town clothes.

Sometimes
he wears his
golfing clothes

or his evening clothes

or his
boating clothes.

This is how he dressed
when he went flying
with his friend Harry.
Harry is a mole.

"See how the kites fly," said Basil.
"If a kite can fly in the sky,
so can I."

"But you are not a kite," said Harry.
"You are round and heavy.
A kite is thin and light."
"Then I will make a big kite," said Basil.

Basil took a hammer, some nails, some
wood, some string and some paper.
He soon made a kite.

Basil and Harry took the kite to the
top of the hill.

Harry ran very fast down the hill.
He pulled the string and
Basil jumped into the air.

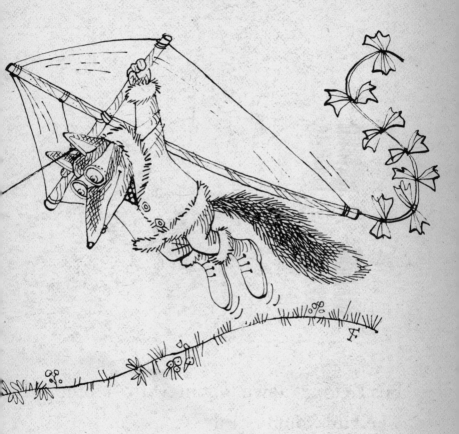

Basil came down again with a bump.
The kite would not fly.
"You are right, old chap," said Basil.
"I am too heavy."

He sat down in the grass. Some seeds
flew from the dandelion clocks.
They flew up into the air.

"See how the dandelion seeds fly,"
said Basil to Harry.
"The seeds are carried by umbrellas.
If a dandelion seed can fly in the sky,
so can I."

"But the seeds are little,"
said Harry. "You are big."
"Then I will make a big umbrella,"
said Basil.

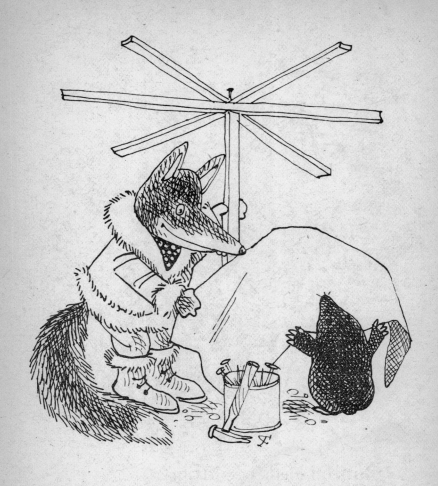

Basil took his hammer, some nails, some
wood, some string and some paper. He
soon made a big umbrella.

Basil climbed a tree and jumped.

The umbrella turned inside out,
and Basil landed with a bump.
He looked up at the crows in the sky.
"See how the crows fly," he said.
"They flap their wings.
If a crow can fly in the sky,
so can I."

"But you have no wings," said Harry.
"Then I will make some wings," said
Basil, "and then I will flap them."

Basil took his hammer, some nails, and
some pieces of wood.
He soon made some wings.

"Now I will try my wings," he said.

He climbed on to a wall.

Then he jumped off, flapping his wings.

Basil did not fly.

He landed among the chickens.

"Wings are no good without feathers,"
he said.

They found some feathers
in the chicken-run.
They fixed them to the wood and Basil
took the wings to the top of the hill.

Basil ran fast down the hill.
He flapped his wings
and jumped into the air.
He did not fly.

He landed in the lake among the ducks.
The ducks were startled. They ran
quickly over the water and flew away.

"See how the ducks fly," said Basil.
"If a duck can fly in the sky,
so can I."
"But you cannot run fast enough,"
said Harry.

"Then I will make a machine," said Basil.
"I will make a machine with wheels
to carry me fast down the hill."
He took his hammer, some nails and
some wood. He fixed the wings to a
bicycle and made a machine.

Basil and Harry took their machine to
the top of the hill.

Basil sat on the bicycle and pedalled
fast down the hill past Harry.
"Now watch me fly," called Basil.

He did not fly.
The machine hit a bump and fell to
pieces.

Basil sat in the grass.

A grasshopper landed on his nose.

Basil sneezed.

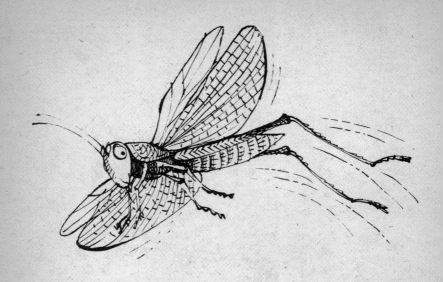

The grasshopper jumped into the air.
It opened its wings and flew away.
"See how the grasshopper flies," said
Basil. "It jumps into the air with its
long jumping legs.
If a grasshopper can fly
so can I."

"But you have no long jumping legs," said Harry.

"Then I will make something else to throw me into the air," said Basil.

They took the broken machine to the
cliff beside the sea.

Basil took his hammer, some nails, some
wood and some elastic and he mended
the machine.

He fixed the elastic to a tree-stump
and made a catapult. He made a giant
catapult to throw him into the air.

"Come with me," said Basil.
"This time we will fly!"

Harry and Basil stood on the machine.
Basil cut the string and the catapult
threw them into the air over the cliff.

Basil and Harry held on tight.
"You see, old chap, I told you so.
We're flying!" cried Basil.
They flew over the sea.

"We're falling!" cried Harry.

They landed with a splash in the sea.

The machine turned upside down and
floated. Basil and Harry climbed on to
it and looked around them at the water.
They saw a helicopter flying past.

Basil made a flag with his scarf and
waved it in the air.

"Help, help!" he called.

The helicopter flew low over them and a man lowered a rope with a hook on it. "Fix the hook to your machine," he called. "We will carry you to the shore."

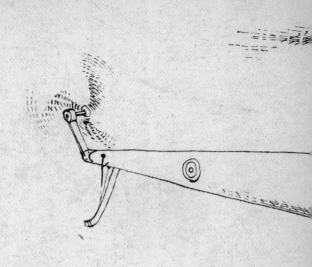

Basil and Harry and their machine
were lifted up out of the water and
carried towards the shore.

Basil looked up at the helicopter.

"See how the helicopter flies," he said . . .

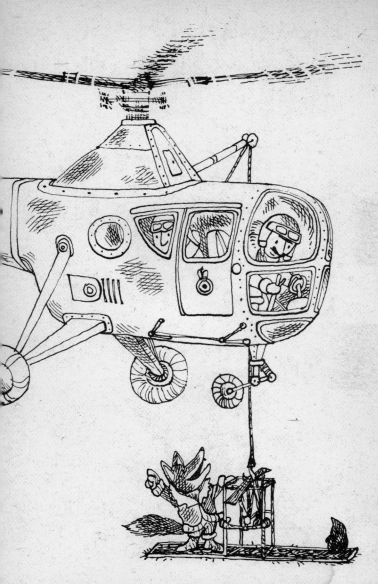

"Yes, I know," said Harry.
"If a helicopter can fly over the sea, so can we!"

the end